Angels

A Lola and Ali
Funtastical Adventure

Lola Jordan Grant

LOLA JORDAN GRANT

BOOK PUBLISHERS NETWORK
Changing the World One Book at a Time

Book Publishers Network
P. O. Box 2256
Bothell, WA 98041
425-483-3040
www.bookpublishersnetwork.com

Printed in the U.S.A.

10 9 8 7 6 5 4 3 2 1

ISBN: 978-1-945271-29-8

LCCN: 2016962779

Dear Friend,

My name is Lola, and this is me with my dog, Ali. She and I have a lot of super FUNTASTICAL adventures together. (BTW, FUNTASTICAL is a word I made up . . . because it is fun to say!) This book is about one of our great adventures, and I really hope it inspires YOU! Happy reading!

Love, Lola

Have you ever seen an angel? No?
Me either.
But I dream about one all the time.

I call him John the Angel.
In my dreams,
He teaches me lessons
From a magical book
About how to make my life an ADVENTURE.

Brave every challenge.

Enjoy life as an adventure.

Keep your promises.

Invent ways to love.

Never give up.

Dream BIG!

When I was six and wondering,
"Is God real?"
He told me there are angels
Living all over the Earth disguised as humans.

He told me I had to learn to see them
To get my question answered.

Then he wrote a poem
To teach me how to do it.

How to See
Human Angels

(Find each missing word hidden in the pictures.)

Human _ _ _ _ _ _ are all around
And if we look hard
They can be found.

Climb _ _ _ _ _ _ _ _ _ _ _ _ _ and you will see
Examples that show us how to be
More loving to those who are in need.

Angel Mountain

feed

They find the lost, those most in need.
They help the homeless
And the hungry, _ _ _ _.

When children cry and no one hears
These angels reach out
And dry their _ _ _ _ _.

tears

All who give help or a helping _ _ _ _
Are angels on Earth
Walking upon the land.

They help us believe in a better way
Bringing hope and _ _ _ _ _
To every day.

BRING HOPE AND LIGHT TO EVERY DAY

To see and love them, you must do
Acts selfless and _ _ _ _
To help others, too.

Then your eyes will be opened
And your heart will see
A better way for us all to _ _.

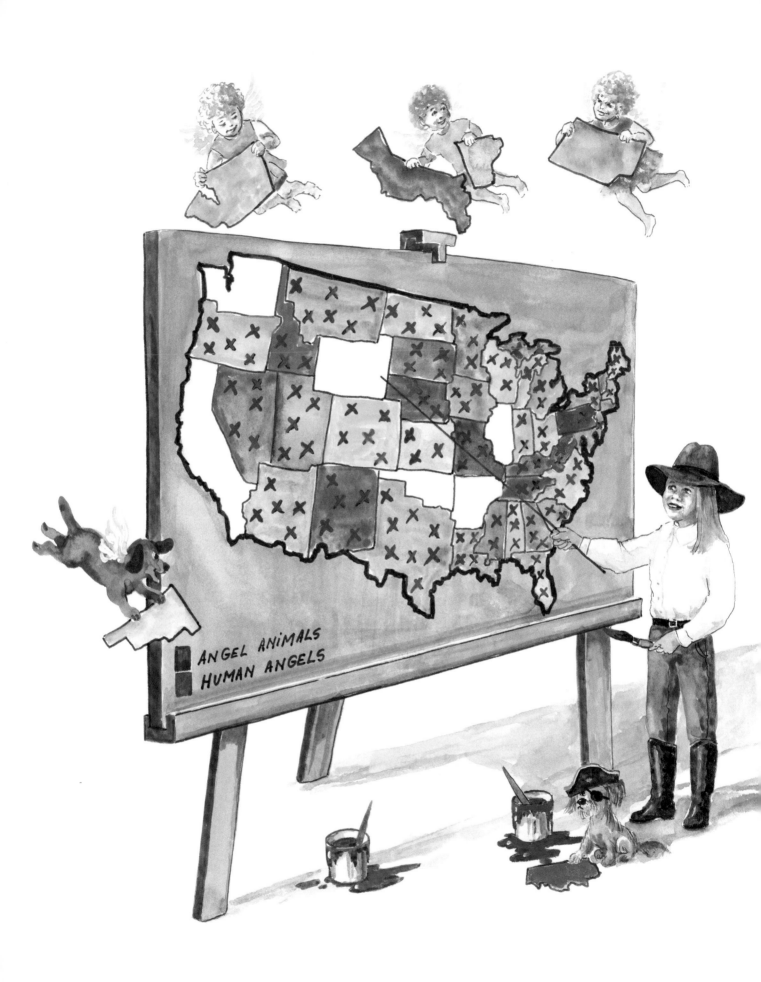

ANGEL ANIMALS
HUMAN ANGELS

This poem is like a puzzle
Or a clue to a hidden treasure.
See if you can figure it out.

Once I understood the poem,
I started to see Human Angels everywhere.

Now, when I find a Human Angel,
like magic,
God is right there in front of me.

Earn your angel wings!

Become a Human Angel Project Investigator.
Help us look for Human Angels.

Go to my website: www.look4angels.com.
Tell us the story of a Human Angel you know.

Here is how to become a "H.A.P.I." Agent!

H.A.P.I.
Human Angel Project Investigator

Becoming a H.A.P.I. AGENT means you learn how to see human angels all around you. You won't see them wearing wings or halos, but they ARE AROUND EVERWHERE to help people (and animals, too). Here is what you can do now:

1. Anyone you see being kind to others might be a Human Angel. Even if you don't know the person's name, write and tell me what you saw at www.look4angels.com.

2. Human Angels tend to hang out in places like food banks and other charities that help people. Go visit one of these charities and ask if they have a person they want to nominate as a Human Angel. Ask to meet that person so you can learn his or her story.

3. Ask your family if they know Human Angels. Then ask them to introduce you so you discover more about what they do, so you can tell their story here.

4. Ask your teacher if you can have a Human Angel come tell his or her story to your class. Then ask your teacher to invite everyone in class to help find a Human Angel story. Please share those stories with me at www.look4angels.com!

www.look4angels.com

- LOS ANGELES AUTHOR -
LOLA JORDAN GRANT

HOME | FIND ANGELS | BE ANGELS | BOOK | BIO | TOONS | STORIES | CONTACT | SHOP

Welcome To My Website!

H.A.P.I.
Human Angel Project Investigator

I'm looking for GREAT stories about Human Angels.

My name is Lola Jordan Grant, author of *ANGELS: A Lola and Ali Funtastical Adventure*. My book is about how my dog, Ali, and I learned to see Human Angels. It turns out these people are everywhere, and they perform loving acts of kindness all the time. I want to SPREAD THAT LOVE AROUND!

Will you help me do that? Look4Angels.com is your place to share stories about Human Angels THAT YOU FIND . . .IN YOUR FAMILY, IN THE PARK, IN THE GROCERY STORE . . . OR ANYWHERE! Just go to the STORIES page on this website and tell me in your own words a Human Angel story that you know.

START YOUR H.A.P.I. QUEST

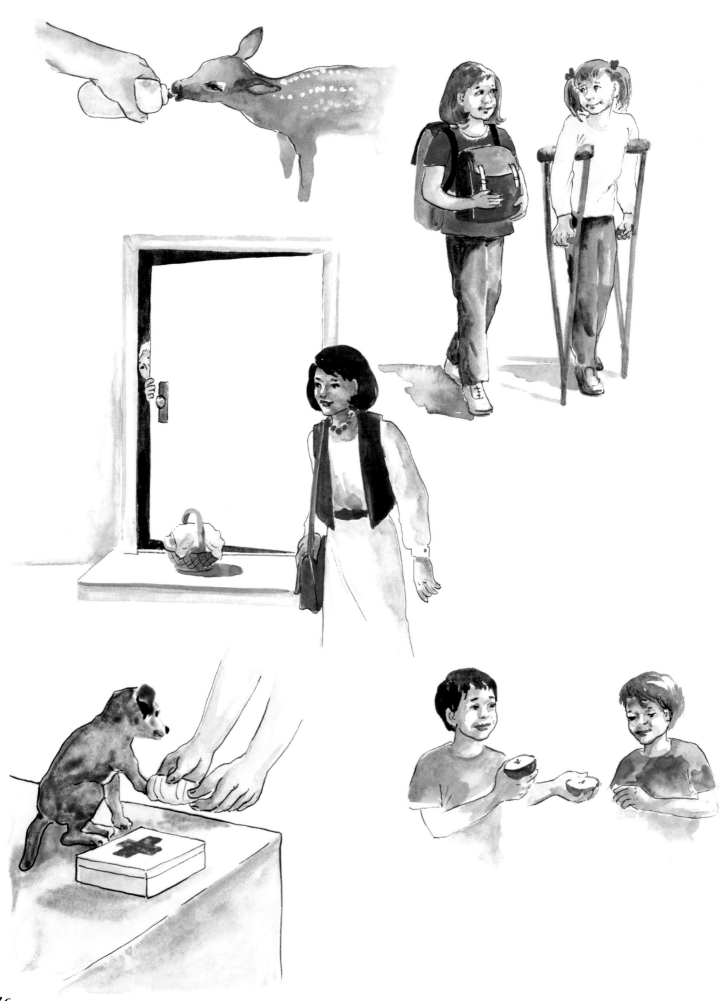

How to become a Human Angel yourself!

Not only can you become a H.A.P.I. Agent and learn to spot Human Angels; you can also learn to become a Human Angel yourself. Here are just some of the ways:

1. Give a homeless person a dollar.

2. Raise money for your favorite cause by hosting a lemonade stand or other fundraiser.

3. Volunteer at a charity or church event.

4. Write a letter to a soldier.

5. Hug someone who is sad.

6. Rescue an animal.

7. Smile at someone who seems to be having a bad day.

8. Help a blind person walk across the street.

9. Listen to a senior citizen who might be lonely.

10. Share your lunch with someone who is hungry.

Let us know what YOU come up with to help others!